ST. ALPHONSUS SCHOOL

**FRANCES BERRES**

*Assistant Director, Clinic School*
*University of California*
*at Los Angeles*

**JAMES C. COLEMAN**

*Associate Professor of Psychology*
*Director, Clinic School*
*University of California at Los Angeles*

**WILLIAM S. BRISCOE**

*Professor of Education*
*University of California*
*at Los Angeles*

**FRANK M. HEWETT**

*Supervisor, Clinic School*
*University of California*
*at Los Angeles*

Bill          Salty          Andy

*Illustrations by JOSEPH MANISCALCO*

# Submarine Rescue

Commander Gray  Dan  Carlos

HARR WAGNER PUBLISHING COMPANY • San Francisco

# TABLE of CONTENTS

*Chapter One*

## BILL'S LETTER

The morning sun came down on the deck of the *Sea Watch*. The boat had just pulled away from the dock at the Navy base.

The *Sea Watch* moved slowly through the water for some time. Two men stood in the bow of the boat. They held a long tube out over the water. The long tube had a cable on it. The cable came back over the deck of the *Sea Watch.* The long tube was a torpedo detector. The crew of the *Sea Watch* was looking for a torpedo on the bottom of the sea. The torpedo detector would tell them when the boat came over the torpedo.

"Stop here, Bill!" called Dan. "This must be the right place. The torpedo detector has found a torpedo for us down there."

"All right," Bill called back. He brought the *Sea Watch* to a stop in the water.

"Here goes the anchor," said Andy. He let the anchor of the *Sea Watch* down into the water. After the anchor went down to the sea bottom, it held the boat in one place.

"Here goes our first dive for the Navy," said Carlos. "Are you ready to go down, Dan?"

"I am," answered Dan. "Help me get my diving suit and helmet on."

◁○ ◁○ ◁○ ◁○ ◁○

The *Sea Watch* was a diving boat. It was Dan's boat. From the boat, divers went down and worked under the water. Dan and Carlos were the divers on the *Sea Watch*.

Bill ran the *Sea Watch* for Dan. Bill took the boat out to sea where the diving took place. He helped Dan and Carlos when they were diving, too.

Andy was another member of the crew. He was not a diver. Andy did many things to help on the *Sea Watch*. But the big thing he did was to cook.

Diving and working on a boat make men like to eat. They like to eat good food. Andy was a good cook, and the men liked his cooking.

2

There was one other member of the crew on the *Sea Watch*.

"Ahoy!" he said. "Ahoy!"

This was Salty. He was Andy's parrot.

"Diving for a torpedo is something we have not done before," said Andy, as he brought the helmet out to Dan. "I would not like to have a torpedo go off up here on the *Sea Watch*."

"There goes Andy again," laughed Carlos. "He always finds something to worry about."

"Do not worry, Andy," said Dan. "The torpedo I find down there will not go off. It is a training torpedo. It is only used by the Navy to train men. It is not like a real torpedo found in a submarine."

"But the Navy wants it back," said Bill, "so it can be used over again. The torpedo detector finds the torpedo, and it can be used over and over again."

"That is all right then," said Andy. "But I would not like to work on a submarine. I would not like to be under the water with a real torpedo. No, sir, a submarine is not the place for me."

"No, sir," said Salty. "No, sir."

"The men on a submarine would like to have you with them, Andy," laughed Bill. "They would like

3

your cooking. I know. I have been in the Navy. I have been out on many submarines. The men like good food."

"Do they get it?" asked Carlos.

"Yes, they do," answered Bill. "The crew of a submarine gets all the food it needs and wants. The Navy has the best for its men."

"I know that they train some of the best men in the Navy for the submarines," said Dan.

"How about it, Andy?" asked Carlos. "Why not go to work as a cook on a submarine?"

"No, thank you," answered Andy. "I will work on top of the water."

The other men laughed at Andy. But they all liked him very much. The crew of the *Sea Watch* liked to work together. And they liked to laugh.

"I have to get down there and look for that torpedo," said Dan. "We must get our work done for the Navy."

The Navy had asked Dan and the crew of the *Sea Watch* to work for them for a time. The Navy was training men in the use of the torpedo at the Navy base. When a torpedo was shot out into the water, the Navy told Dan about where it would stop. Then the *Sea Watch* would take the torpedo detector out and find the torpedo.

4

Bill and Andy helped Dan put on his diving suit. Then they helped him put on his diving helmet. The air pump had been started, and it would give Dan all the air he needed. The air went through the air hose and into his helmet. The men could see that the air hose was working all right.

Dan was helped over the side of the boat. He slowly went down into the water. Soon the men could not see the top of Dan's helmet. He was going down deep into the water. Dan had a cable with him to hook on to the torpedo when he found it. The torpedo could then be pulled up and put on the deck of the *Sea Watch.*

Carlos watched the air pump. He watched to see that Dan got all the air he needed.

Bill held on to Dan's rope. He could tell when Dan got to the bottom. Then the rope would stop pulling.

Now Bill held the rope and waited. He waited to get a signal from Dan. Dan would signal by pulling on his rope. He would signal when he wanted more air or when he wanted to be pulled up.

"How long will it take Dan?" asked Andy.

"I do not know," answered Carlos. "The torpedo could have gone down into the mud. If it did, it will take Dan time to find it."

MANISCALCO

The men waited for some time. Then Bill got a signal from Dan. There were four pulls on the rope. This was the signal to pull Dan up. Bill slowly pulled on the rope. He pulled it up over the side of the *Sea Watch*. Soon, he saw the top of Dan's helmet down through the water. Andy got ready to help pull Dan up, too. As Dan came up to the top of the water, Andy and Bill pulled him up to the deck.

Soon Dan stood on the deck of the *Sea Watch*. Water ran down from his diving suit. Andy worked fast to take off Dan's helmet. Bill put the air hose and rope in place on the deck. Then he helped Andy pull the heavy helmet off of Dan.

"The torpedo detector was right," said Dan, after his helmet was off. "I found the torpedo down there. I hooked the cable on it. It is ready now to be pulled up to the *Sea Watch*."

After helping Dan get out of his diving suit, the crew pulled the torpedo up to the boat. When it was in place on the deck, Dan told Bill to take the *Sea Watch* on through the water.

As the day went by, the men found one torpedo after another. The torpedo detector would tell them where to dive. Then Dan or Carlos would dive down and hook the cable on the torpedo. At last, every training torpedo was on the deck of the *Sea Watch*.

"We can go back to the Navy base now," said Dan. "The last torpedo we were looking for has been pulled up. Radio the Navy base that we are coming in, Carlos."

Carlos went to the radio. He called the Navy base and said the *Sea Watch* had found the last torpedo.

The anchor was pulled up, and the boat started back to the Navy base. Soon the *Sea Watch* was at the Navy dock. The Navy had men there ready to go to work. They took every torpedo off the deck of the *Sea Watch*.

Then Dan saw Commander Gray of the Navy base coming down the dock to the *Sea Watch*.

"Hello, Commander Gray," called Dan.

"Hello, Dan," said Commander Gray. "I see that you found what you went out looking for."

"Yes, sir," said Dan.

"Good," said Commander Gray. He held up a letter he had. "This is for you, Bill," he said.

Bill took the letter and opened it.

"What is it, Bill?" asked Dan.

"It is from the submarine base here," answered Bill. "I have been called back into the Navy. I am to go and help train a new crew on the submarine *Sunfin*."

*Chapter Two*

## ANDY RUNS THE SEA WATCH

Bill looked at the letter again.

"So I will be going out on the *Sunfin* this time," he said. "I have heard it is a good submarine."

"It is the best submarine in the Navy," laughed Commander Gray. "I should know. The *Sunfin* is my submarine."

Bill looked up. "I did not know that, sir," he said.

"Yes," said Commander Gray. "And I will tell you why this letter came to you as it did. We are going out for some training dives in the morning. At the last minute, one of my top crew members was called away. I needed another man who knows submarines to help me train some new Navy men. I knew you had worked on submarines before, Bill, so I asked the Navy to call you back."

"Thank you, sir," said Bill. "I will like going out on a submarine again." Then he looked at Dan. "I do not like to be away from my work on the *Sea Watch*. But when the Navy needs me, I am always ready to help."

"Do you need a good cook on the *Sunfin*?" asked Carlos. "Andy said he wanted to go to work on a submarine."

"Submarine," said Salty. "Submarine."

Dan and Bill and Carlos laughed.

"No, sir," said Andy. "That is not right. I would not like to work under the water."

"We cannot let Andy go," said Dan. "With Bill gone, Andy will have to run the *Sea Watch* for us."

"Then I will watch him run it from the dock," laughed Carlos. "I do not want to be on the boat when Andy runs it."

"You will see," said Andy. "I know how to run the boat just the way Bill does."

"I must get back up to the base now," said Commander Gray. "I will see you on the *Sunfin* in the morning, Bill."

He walked up the dock. The crew of the *Sea Watch* stood on deck talking for a time.

"I will have to go in the morning," said Bill. "But I should be back soon. The Navy has not called me back for too long a time. Keep the *Sea Watch* going for me, Andy."

"You should have said, 'Keep it on top of the water,'" laughed Carlos. "You cannot tell where Andy will take the *Sea Watch*."

In the morning, all the men but Bill were back at the *Sea Watch* ready to go to work. Andy was in Bill's place ready to take the *Sea Watch* out to sea. Carlos pulled in the line that held the *Sea Watch* to the dock.

"Take the *Sea Watch* out, Andy," called Dan.

Andy started the motor. He ran it fast, but the boat did not move.

"What is the trouble, Andy?" called Dan.

Andy ran the motor very fast, but the *Sea Watch* only moved slowly away from the dock. Andy started to worry.

"What is the trouble?" said Salty. "What is the trouble?"

"I don't know," said Andy. "This is the way Bill always gets the *Sea Watch* going."

Just then, he heard something. He looked up and saw Carlos in the bow of the boat. Carlos was laughing.

"Andy cannot get the *Sea Watch* away from the dock," laughed Carlos.

12

Then Andy saw something. He stopped the motor and ran up to the bow of the boat.

"So this is it," he said. "I see now why I could not get the *Sea Watch* to move very fast."

Andy looked where Carlos stood. The anchor line was over the side. Carlos had let the anchor down. This had made the *Sea Watch* move very slowly.

Carlos laughed again.

"It was all in fun, Andy," he said.

"All in fun," said Salty. "All in fun."

But Andy did not answer. He pulled the anchor up and went back to the motor. This time the *Sea Watch* moved out fast from the dock.

⋘⋙ ⋘⋙ ⋘⋙ ⋘⋙ ⋘⋙

As the day went by, the *Sea Watch* found one torpedo after another. After every torpedo was put on deck, Dan had Carlos pull up the anchor. Then Andy was told to take the boat on through the water to look for another torpedo.

Just after another torpedo had been found, Dan called to Carlos and Andy, "Take the *Sea Watch* on."

Carlos pulled up the anchor. Andy started the motor. Then Carlos stood up on the side of the boat to see if the anchor was in place.

"Can you get the boat going this time ..." he called back to Andy.

But before he was through talking, Andy had started the boat up fast in the water. He made a very fast start. Carlos went off the boat and into the water with a big splash!

Andy looked back. Then he stopped the boat. There was Carlos in the water. He called out to Andy as he swam up to the *Sea Watch*.

"I will get you for this, Andy."

Andy laughed and laughed. Andy and Dan helped Carlos back up on the boat.

Carlos started after Andy.

"Let me at him," he said.

But Dan stopped him.

"It was all in fun," said Andy.

"All in fun," said Salty, the parrot. "All in fun."

"I don't want any more trouble with you two," laughed Dan.

Dan looked at Andy. Dan could tell why Andy had started up the *Sea Watch* so fast. Dan laughed and laughed.

"All right now," he said. "Let us get on with the work."

16

*Chapter Three*

## THE SUNFIN IN TROUBLE

That morning, before the sun came up, Bill was on the *Sunfin* ready to work. He walked up on the deck of the submarine and then went down inside. He saw that Commander Gray had come on the *Sunfin* before him.

"Good morning, sir," Bill said.

"Good morning, Bill," said Commander Gray. "The new Navy men will be coming soon. But before they do, I want you to know the other crew members."

Commander Gray took Bill around the submarine. Bill got to know the crew members who were going to help train the new Navy men. Soon the new Navy men came down inside the submarine.

"I want you to take some of the new men through the submarine," Commander Gray said to Bill. He told Bill what every one of the new men was to do.

Bill then took the new men through the submarine.

There is not much room inside a submarine. From bow to stern the men do not have much room to move around. There is not enough room for all the crew to work at one time. Some crew members work as others eat or sleep. That way, there are always crew members who are ready to work.

Work inside a submarine must go on all the time. Every man must know just what to do. The men must work together at all times.

When every one of the new crew members was in his place, Bill went back to Commander Gray.

"They all know where to stand watch, sir," he said. "And the other members of the *Sunfin's* crew are standing by to help them."

"Good," said Commander Gray. "We are ready to take the *Sunfin* out to sea."

"I will stand watch at my place in the stern," said Bill. He walked back through the submarine to the stern.

Commander Gray took a telephone and called to the men in the ship. They all stood by to help take the *Sunfin* away from the dock. Some of the crew went out on deck. They pulled the lines in from the deck. Soon the *Sunfin* moved slowly out to sea.

The *Sunfin* went on and on through the water. After a time, the submarine was at the place for the first dive.

Commander Gray stood on the deck of the *Sunfin*. Three of his crew members stood with him. They were the lookouts for the *Sunfin*. They looked out over the sea from all sides as the submarine moved through the water.

"How does it look?" asked Commander Gray.

"All right from here, sir," answered one of the lookouts.

"Good," said the commander. "We are ready to dive." Commander Gray took up a telephone.

"Radio back to the Navy base," called Commander Gray to the radio man down inside the submarine. "Radio back that we are ready to make our first dive."

The radio message went out. Then Commander Gray said, "Stand by to dive!"

The message went all through the submarine, "Stand by to dive!" All the *Sunfin's* crew moved very fast to get the submarine ready for the dive.

Up on deck, Commander Gray and the three lookouts started down into the submarine.

Commander Gray watched the three men as they went down inside the submarine. The commander of a submarine must know that all of his men are off the deck before the submarine dives.

When he saw that all of his men were inside, Commander Gray went down into the *Sunfin*. One of the crew members closed the hatch. Now all the crew members of the *Sunfin* were inside the submarine.

One of the *Sunfin's* crew members stood looking at a great many signal lights that were before him. The signal lights told him when all the openings in the submarine were closed. When the crew member saw that all the lights were right, he called out to Commander Gray, "Ready for diving, sir."

"Very good," said the commander. Then he called out to another member, "Air in the boat!"

This crew member let some air out of the *Sunfin's* air tanks. The air shot out under pressure into the submarine.

Then the crew member waited. He watched a gauge before him. The gauge would tell him if any air was escaping from the submarine. If air was escaping, the crew would know the submarine was not closed off from the sea. They would not take the submarine down. For water could run in through the place where the air was escaping.

Commander Gray went over and looked at the gauge. He saw that no air was escaping.

"Pressure in the boat!" Commander Gray called out to the men.

Now the *Sunfin* was ready to dive under the sea. Commander Gray told his men how far down to take the submarine. The crew went right to work.

Slowly the bow of the *Sunfin* started down under the water. The sea splashed up over the top deck of the submarine. In a minute or so, the *Sunfin* would be diving deep under the water.

Commander Gray looked around at his men. They were all working together. Every man had a part in the *Sunfin's* first dive.

One man looked at another gauge that told how deep the *Sunfin* was going. The submarine was all the way under water now. It was going down deeper and deeper.

Just then a call came over the telephone for Commander Gray. A look of worry came over him as he heard the message.

"Water coming through a vent in the stern!" called one of the crew members. "The vent came open as we dived. We cannot get it closed!"

21

Commander Gray looked at the signal lights. They were all right. Something must have gone wrong with one of the vents in the stern. It had not closed right.

The crew of the *Sunfin* did all they could to close the vent, but it was no use.

Commander Gray told the crew to take the submarine up right away. He told the men in the stern to close off that part of the submarine.

"Water coming in very fast, sir!" called the crew member over the telephone. "We . . ." The telephone stopped working. Commander Gray heard no more.

Commander Gray knew that he must get the *Sunfin* to the top of the water fast. He watched the gauge that told how deep the submarine was. Slowly the *Sunfin* moved up through the water. For a minute, it looked as if the submarine would make it.

Then one of the crew members called out, "We have stopped going up, sir!"

Commander Gray looked at the gauge. It told him that the *Sunfin* had started down again. The water coming into the stern had made the submarine too heavy to get back up to the top. The *Sunfin* was going deeper and deeper! There was not a thing the crew could do to stop the dive!

*Chapter Four*

## THE SEA WATCH TO THE RESCUE

The *Sea Watch* was a long way from the Navy base now. The diving boat had found every torpedo, and was about to go back. Dan looked out over the deck. Every torpedo was in place.

"Another day's work done," said Carlos, walking up to Dan.

"That's right," said Dan. "Radio the Navy base that we are coming in now."

Carlos went inside the *Sea Watch* to the radio. He was just about to put the message over the radio when he stopped. There was a message coming in over the radio. Carlos heard the message and took it down. He looked at it for a minute. Then he ran out on deck to give the message to Dan.

"Dan! Dan!" he called. "Look at this!"

U.S. NAVY CALLING ALL SHIPS. U.S. NAVY
CALLING ALL SHIPS. YOUR HELP IS NEEDED.
THE SUBMARINE SUNFIN HAS SUNK.

The radio message went on to ask all ships to go
to the place where the *Sunfin* had sunk. The Navy
asked the ships to be ready to help save the crew of
the *Sunfin*. The Navy rescue ships would be there soon.

"This is real trouble," said Dan.

He went right to the radio. Soon a message was
on its way back to the Navy base.

THE SEA WATCH READY TO HELP. WILL START
FOR PLACE SUNFIN WENT DOWN RIGHT AWAY.

Dan and Carlos went to tell Andy about the message.

"Then the crew members of the *Sunfin* are trapped
on the bottom of the sea," said Andy.

"Bill is trapped down there, too," said Carlos. "I
have heard what it is like to be trapped in a submarine on the bottom of the sea."

"We must move fast," said Dan. "The message told
just where the *Sunfin* went down. We are not far from
there now. We could be the first ship there."

"I don't like the looks of the water," said Andy.
"We could be in for a heavy fog."

Dan and Carlos looked out over the water. They could see a gray fog starting to come in.

"Let's hope it does not come in," said Dan. "We must move fast!"

Dan told Andy to take the *Sea Watch* to the place where the *Sunfin* had sunk.

The boat moved fast through the water. Dan and Carlos stood on deck. They did not talk to one another. But they were worrying about Bill and the crew of the *Sunfin*, trapped down on the bottom of the sea. They were worrying about the gray fog coming in around them, too.

The *Sunfin* had come to a stop in the mud on the bottom of the sea. There was no sound in the dark, deep water. Every now and then, air would escape from a part of the submarine and slowly start up to the top of the water.

Inside the *Sunfin*, Commander Gray stood with some of his men.

"It is no use," he said slowly. "We cannot get the *Sunfin* up from here. Too much water has come in. We cannot pump it out."

Then he looked at one of his men. "Let go the telephone buoy," he told him.

"Yes, sir," the man said.

Soon a big buoy started to float up from the deck of the *Sunfin*. It was let up on a cable. The buoy would float when it got to the top of the water. There was a telephone inside the buoy. With this telephone, the rescue ships could talk to the men trapped inside the submarine.

"Now man the signal gun," called Commander Gray.

On the top deck of the *Sunfin* was a signal gun. It could be shot from inside the submarine. Smoke signals could be shot up to the top of the water from the gun. The smoke signals would go off in the air. They would make a heavy smoke. Rescue ships could see the smoke from far away. It would tell them where to find the telephone buoy. The smoke would tell them where the submarine had sunk, too.

The crew member shot a smoke signal up with the signal gun.

"Now we must wait," said Commander Gray. "By now the Navy must know we are in trouble. They were waiting for a radio message from us when we came up from the dive."

Commander Gray looked at his watch.

"After so much time has gone by," he said, "they will know we must have sunk."

"Our last radio message to the base told where we were," said the radio man. "And we have not moved."

"The radio does not do us any good now," said another man. "It will not work under the water."

"That's right," said Commander Gray. "We can only hope that the rescue ships see the smoke signals and find the telephone buoy right away."

The crew member shot off the signal gun again. The smoke signal shot up to the top of the water and went off. It made a heavy smoke.

Up on the *Sea Watch*, Dan and Carlos were talking.

"From what the Navy's message told us," said Dan, "we are very close to the place where the *Sunfin* went down. Keep a lookout for a smoke signal from the submarine, Carlos."

Carlos went out on deck to look for a smoke signal. After a time, he ran back in where Dan was.

Dan looked up. "Did you see the smoke signal?" he asked.

"No," answered Carlos. "But I did see something I do not like at all. The fog is coming in all around us."

Dan went out on deck. He saw what Carlos was talking about. The gray fog was coming in very close around them.

"We cannot see a thing in this fog," Dan said. "All we can do is wait for it to let up."

Down in the *Sunfin*, Commander Gray and his men waited and waited. They talked about what had gone wrong when the *Sunfin* made its dive.

"The signal lights were on, all right," said Commander Gray. "But something went wrong. The air vents in the stern did not close."

"It all took place very fast, sir," said one of the crew members who had escaped from the stern. "Not a thing we did stopped the water from coming in."

Commander Gray looked at the members of the crew who stood around him.

"Not all of the crew is here," he said slowly. "We waited to close off the stern as long as we could, but some of our men were left back there."

The men did not talk for a minute. Then Commander Gray went on, "I only hope the others made it to the escape room in the stern in time. If they did, they are waiting there just as we are waiting here."

"We have no way of knowing, sir," said one of the crew. "The telephone line is not working."

"Do not talk from now on if you do not have to," said Commander Gray to his men. "And do not move around the submarine. This will help us breathe more slowly. The more slowly we breathe, the more air we will save."

He walked over to the air tanks hooked on to the side of the *Sunfin*.

"All the air we have to breathe is in here," he said. "When it is gone we are in real trouble."

Up on the *Sea Watch*, Dan and Carlos looked out into the fog.

"It's no use," said Carlos. "I cannot see a thing."

"Keep looking," said Dan. "We are very close now."

The two men walked around the deck of the *Sea Watch* and looked for some signal from the *Sunfin*. Andy took the boat very slowly through the water.

After a time, the fog started to let up. The men

33

could see out over the water again. Dan was in the bow when he heard Carlos call out.

"Look! Out there! I see something!"

Dan ran to where Carlos stood.

"Is that more fog?" asked Carlos.

"No," came the answer. "It's too dark for fog. Carlos, it's a smoke signal!"

"Then we have found the *Sunfin*," said Carlos.

"Take the *Sea Watch* over there, Andy," called Dan. Then he said to Carlos, "The telephone buoy will be over there, too. We must let the crew of the *Sunfin* know we are here."

Andy took the *Sea Watch* slowly through the water. Soon Dan saw the telephone buoy floating in the water. He and Carlos pulled it up on the deck of the *Sea Watch*.

On the buoy it said:

SUBMARINE SUNK HERE. U.S.S. SUNFIN.
TELEPHONE INSIDE.

Dan opened the buoy and took out the telephone. He signaled to the *Sunfin* that the buoy had been found.

But the men inside the *Sunfin*, deep down in the water, did not need the signal to tell them that the telephone buoy had been found. They had heard the sound of the motor of the *Sea Watch*. The sound had come down to them through the water.

"A ship has found us," said Commander Gray.

He took up the telephone.

"Hello," he said slowly. "This is Commander Gray."

"Hello, Commander Gray," Dan said. "The *Sea Watch* is here. The Navy rescue ships are on the way. We are here to help in any way we can."

"Good," said Commander Gray. "Now that you are here we will start coming up with the escape lung."

"How are your crew members?" asked Dan.

"Some of them were trapped in the stern where the water came in," answered the commander. "We do not know if they made it to the escape room in the stern or not."

Dan wanted to ask about Bill, but he did not. All the men in the *Sunfin* were in real trouble. Bill was only one of them.

"We will be waiting for your men to get to the top," said Dan. He put the telephone back in the buoy. Then he told Carlos and Andy what had been said.

"I hope Bill will be one of the first men we see come up," said Carlos.

Dan and Andy hoped Bill would come up soon, too.

"It will not be dark for a time," said Dan. "Let's hope we can get all the *Sunfin's* crew up before then."

"Look!" said Carlos. "Out there over the water. The Navy's coming."

Dan and Andy looked up. The fog was not so heavy now. They saw three Navy rescue ships coming fast through the water.

"Good," said Dan. "The Navy is here to start the rescue. We will do all that we can to help them."

Down in the *Sunfin*, Commander Gray talked to his men. "You have been trained for a time like this," he said. "The escape lung will save all of us if we use our training right. Put the escape lung on and get ready to go into the escape chamber."

The escape lung is a small bag of air with a tube coming out of it. The lung hooks around a man's chest. The man can breathe through the tube and use the air in the bag.

In the top part of the bow of the *Sunfin* was an escape chamber. It was from this chamber that the crew hoped to escape.

The men went up through a hatch in the top part of the submarine. Commander Gray held the hatch open and looked up into the escape chamber.

"You men know what to do," he said. "After I close this hatch, start to let in water from the sea. When the water is part way up in the chamber, start pumping in the air. The air will come into the chamber under pressure from the *Sunfin's* air tanks. Soon you will see that the water will stop coming in. The air pressure will be so great that it will keep more water from coming in. Then it will be time to open the escape hatch."

The men in the escape chamber looked around the chamber. They saw the escape hatch. Through it they could escape out into the sea.

"Look and see that the escape lungs you have on are working right," said Commander Gray. "From inside the submarine we have let a line up from the escape hatch. It goes from the escape hatch to the top of the water where it is held by a buoy. You are to go up this line."

The men looked at the escape lungs. They were all working. The commander looked slowly around the chamber at his men.

"Let's go, men," he said. "Take off!"

"All right, sir," one of them said. "Here we go!"

Commander Gray closed the hatch. Then he looked around at the men who were left with him in the submarine.

"Let's hope all goes right in the escape chamber. If it does, we will soon be on our way to the top."

Inside the escape chamber, water came in fast from the sea. Soon the air pressure held it back, and the men opened the escape hatch. They took the line and started up to the top of the water.

The Navy rescue ships had found the buoy that had come up from the escape hatch of the *Sunfin*. They had a small boat by the buoy, ready to help the men of the *Sunfin* out of the water.

The escape hatch at the top of the escape chamber was closed by the last man to go out of the chamber. Now the bottom hatch of the escape chamber could be opened. As it was opened, the water that had been let in ran out. It ran down into the submarine.

Commander Gray told some more men to go up into the chamber. He closed the hatch and waited. He hoped that all of his men would be on the top of the water before long.

One by one the men went up the line that had been let up from the deck of the *Sunfin*. Every man breathed in and out through the escape lung as he went up the line. He stopped every now and then to get used to the new pressure of the water around him. This is just what a deep-sea diver does when he comes up through the water. A diver stops on the way from time to time so he will not get the bends.

The first man who had used the escape chamber saw he was close to the top of the water. He was very glad to know he had escaped from the *Sunfin* and would soon be saved.

As he swam up to the top, he saw some men in the small boat waiting to help him out of the water. Soon he was on the deck of one of the rescue ships.

"How are you?" asked the Navy rescue commander.

"I am all right, sir," said the man.

"Good," said the rescue commander. "I only hope that Commander Gray and the other men with him in the escape chamber in the bow can get up here with the escape lung."

"I hope Bill is one of them," Carlos said.

Dan, Carlos, and Andy had come on the Navy ship to watch the rescue.

"We will just have to wait and see," said Dan. "He could be coming up any minute now."

"I have been looking at every man that comes up," said Andy. "So far, Bill has not been one of them."

The three men looked out over the water to where the small Navy boat was helping the *Sunfin* crew out of the water. A great many of the men had been pulled out and were now on the deck of one of the rescue ships.

Just then, another man swam up to the top. As they saw him, the Navy men in the rescue ship started talking together. Dan, Andy, and Carlos knew who he was, too.

It was Commander Gray!

The men of the *Sea Watch* knew Commander Gray would be the last man to come up from the escape chamber in the bow. Now they knew that Bill had not made it to the bow of the *Sunfin* when the submarine went down!

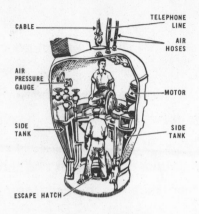

CABLE

TELEPHONE LINE

AIR HOSES

AIR PRESSURE GAUGE

MOTOR

SIDE TANK

SIDE TANK

ESCAPE HATCH

*Chapter Five*

## THE STORM

The crew of the *Sea Watch* looked at one another. But they did not talk.

"That's Commander Gray," the rescue commander called out to them. "That lets us know all the men made it up from the bow." Then he walked over to where Dan, Carlos, and Andy stood.

"I know Bill was not one of the men who came up," he said slowly. "But don't give up hope. We have not looked into the stern escape room. The other crew members could have made it there in time."

"How are you going to look into the stern escape room?" asked Andy.

"With the rescue chamber," came the answer. "We have it on one of our rescue ships. We will pull it down over the escape hatch on the stern of the *Sunfin*.

Then we will open the hatch to see if any more of the crew are inside."

"Then the bow escape chamber is not the only place where a submarine crew can be saved," said Carlos.

"That's right," said the rescue commander. "There is another room in the stern that can be used as an escape chamber."

Then he looked at Dan.

"We will need your help now, Dan," he said. "The rescue chamber runs up and down on a cable. We need you to dive down and hook the cable on the escape hatch in the stern of the *Sunfin*. When the cable is hooked on, the rescue chamber will be ready to use."

"I am ready to go down right away," said Dan.

The rescue commander looked out over the water. The sun was going down. It would be dark soon.

"There is no time left now," he said. "We will have to wait. But we will start to work the first thing in the morning."

"What about the air in the stern?" asked Carlos. "Will it last that long?"

"That's one thing we don't know," came the answer.

"But we cannot go on with the rescue after dark."

The rescue commander started to walk away. "See you first thing in the morning," he called back.

The men of the *Sea Watch* stood for a minute looking down into the water.

"I hope Bill is all right," said Dan.

"So do I," said Carlos.

"I don't like the looks of the water," said Andy. "A storm could come any time now."

"Let's hope it is just more fog," said Dan.

"Stop worrying, Andy," said Carlos. "It looks like only more fog to me, too."

Then the three men went back to the *Sea Watch*.

Soon it was dark. The men of the *Sea Watch* had trouble sleeping. They did not know if they would see Bill again.

In the morning, just as the sun was coming up, the Navy started the rescue work. The rescue commander came over to the *Sea Watch*.

"You can dive down from our ship that has the rescue chamber on it," he said to Dan. "The cable is ready to be hooked on to the *Sunfin*."

Soon Dan, Carlos, and Andy were on the deck of the Navy ship. Carlos and Andy helped Dan get ready. Just before his helmet was put on, Dan asked Andy for a hammer.

"A hammer?" asked Andy. "What do you want a hammer for?"

"I want to take a hammer down with me when I dive," answered Dan. "I will tap out a message in code on the stern of the *Sunfin*. If a message is tapped back, we will know there are crew members inside."

The rescue commander heard Dan and Andy talking.

"Good, Dan," he said. "That will tell us right away if the other crew members are all right."

One of the Navy men brought Dan a hammer. The rescue chamber cable was brought over to Dan, too.

"Hook the cable on the top of the escape hatch," said the rescue commander. "You will find the hatch on the stern of the *Sunfin*."

"All right, sir," said Dan. "I am ready to go down."

Dan's helmet was put in place. He was helped over the side of the ship and down into the water.

Slowly Dan started to go down. He went down and down under the water. At last Dan saw he was on the bottom. He started looking for the *Sunfin* right away. It was not long before he saw it. It looked like a great long fish sleeping in the mud on the bottom of the sea.

Dan walked up to the side of the submarine. He worked his way to the deck of the *Sunfin* and slowly walked to the stern. Soon Dan saw he was over the escape room.

There was the hatch he was looking for.

Dan hooked the rescue chamber cable on the hatch. When he was through, he tapped on the *Sunfin's* stern with the hammer. As he tapped, Dan hoped very much there would be an answer. An answer tapped from inside would tell him the other members of the *Sunfin's* crew were all right.

Dan waited for a time. No answer came back. Dan tapped again and again. He waited. He waited to see if a message would be tapped back by the men inside the *Sunfin*.

As the time went by and no message came back, Dan started to worry. Had the other men of the crew been trapped in the water? Had Bill been trapped with them?

Then Dan heard something coming from the inside of the submarine.

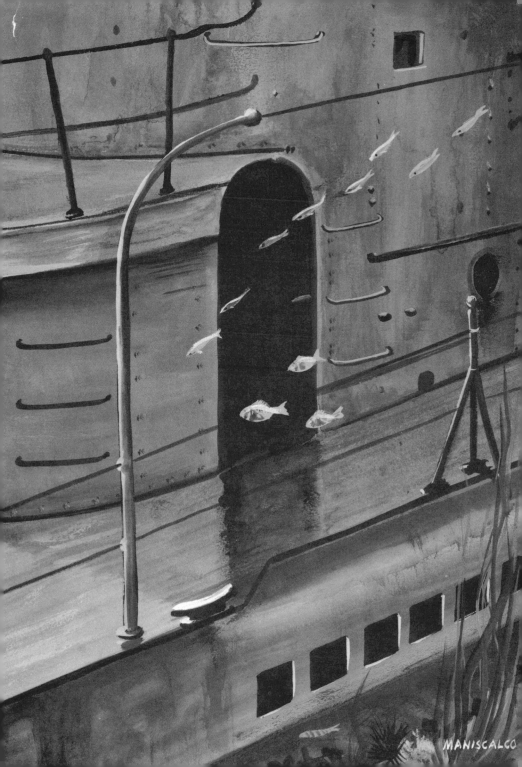

The sound came out to him through the water. It was an answer coming from inside the submarine!

Dan did not wait another minute. He tapped a message in code to the men inside.

HOW...ARE...YOU? HAVE...JUST...HOOKED...
CABLE...ON...HATCH. RESCUE...CHAMBER...
WILL...BE...RIGHT...DOWN.

Dan waited for an answer. Slowly, a code message came back to him.

MEN...ARE...ALL...RIGHT...BUT...AIR...
GOING...FAST.

How glad Dan was to get that message! There were some men left in the *Sunfin* who were all right. Dan hoped Bill was one of them. But he had no time to find out. He must get back to the Navy rescue ship. He must tell the Navy to get the rescue chamber down there fast.

Dan knew that the rescue chamber did not have much time to get down there to save the men left in the *Sunfin*. He pulled four times on his rope. This was to let Carlos know that he was through diving.

Slowly Dan started going back up in the water. Carlos pulled him up and up through the sea. Dan had to stop from time to time to get used to the new air pressure just as the *Sunfin's* men had done.

Air must be pumped down under great pressure to a diver deep under the water. As a diver is pulled up, this pressure goes down. If it goes down too fast, the diver will get the bends. This is why a diver is stopped from time to time in the water. If he gets used to the new air pressure slowly, he will not get the bends.

At last, Dan was back on the deck of the Navy ship. Carlos and Andy and the Navy rescue commander stood around him. They all wanted to know one thing.

"There are some men in the stern escape room," Dan told them. "They tapped out a message to me. But you must move fast. The air in the stern is about gone." Then Dan saw a look of worry on the men.

"What is it?" he asked them.

"Look!" said Carlos. "Out there over the water. A storm is starting. The rescue chamber cannot go down in the storm. The Navy must wait for the storm to be over before they can save the men left in the *Sunfin!*"

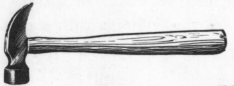

*Chapter Six*

## LAST MAN UP FROM THE SUNFIN

The men of the *Sea Watch* and the crews of the
Navy rescue ships got ready for the storm. Lines
were put around the things on the decks.

The storm came up very fast. Soon water started
splashing up on the sides of the ships. The *Sea Watch*
moved more and more in the water.

"It looks like a big storm," said Dan. "It could
last a long time."

"And there is not much air left in the *Sunfin*," said
Andy. "What a time for a storm to come up!"

The men of the *Sea Watch* and the Navy crew members waited and waited as the storm went on.

Down in the *Sunfin*, the men who were left did not
know why the rescue chamber was not there. They
could not tell that a storm had come. A storm only
makes the sea move on top of the water.

The storm went on all day. But when it got dark, the storm started to let up.

"I hope the Navy can get the rescue chamber down to the *Sunfin* in the morning," said Dan. "If they cannot, there is no hope for the men left there."

"I hope morning will be soon enough," said Carlos. "The air cannot last long down there."

In the morning, the storm was gone. One of the Navy rescue ships put four big anchor buoys out into the water. These anchor buoys held the rescue ship in place so that the rescue chamber could be used.

Then the Navy men hooked the cable on to the bottom of the rescue chamber. It was the cable that Dan had hooked on to the *Sunfin's* hatch. The chamber was put down into the water. Two Navy men were inside to run the chamber up and down on the cable.

Soon the rescue chamber went down under the water. It was on the way to save the last of the *Sunfin's* crew!

Andy, Dan, and Carlos watched what was going on.

"There it goes!" said Andy. "I hope it gets to the men in time."

"Let's hope Bill is one of the men they find down there," said Carlos.

The rescue chamber went down the cable. A motor pulled the cable up into the chamber. Water was let into two side tanks in the chamber so that it was just heavy enough to go down slowly.

At last the rescue chamber was over the hatch on the submarine. Then the chamber was closed down over the escape hatch.

Now the hatch could be opened. The Navy divers in the rescue chamber signaled to the men inside the *Sunfin* to open the hatch.

Slowly the hatch opened. There, down in the escape room of the submarine, were the last men of the *Sunfin*.

"Hello, men," said one of the Navy divers. "Here we are."

The rescue chamber could take all of the men who were left in the submarine. One by one they were helped into the chamber. When they were all in place, the hatches on the submarine and the rescue chamber were closed.

Then the Navy divers shot some of the water in the side tanks out by air pressure. This made the chamber light enough so that it started to go up in the water. The cable was let back out from the rescue chamber as it floated up to the top of the water.

The men inside did not have to worry about the bends. The air pressure in the chamber did not go up or down.

When the rescue chamber got up to the top of the water, it was floating by one of the rescue ships.

All of the Navy men stood at the sides of the ships and looked down at the rescue chamber. Dan, Carlos, and Andy were there, too. They watched the top of the chamber.

"I hope they get it open fast," said Carlos.

He wanted very much to see who was inside.

Dan and Andy wanted to see who was inside, too.

Slowly the hatch on the rescue chamber opened. The first man was helped out. It was not Bill.

One by one the last of the crew of the *Sunfin* were helped out of the chamber. They were then helped up on the deck of the rescue ship.

Dan, Andy, and Carlos looked at every man. They were looking for Bill. Then they saw the last man come up through the hatch opening. They knew who it was!

Carlos called out, "Bill! Bill!"

When Bill had been brought up to the rescue ship's deck, the crew of the *Sea Watch* ran over to him.

"Hello, men," said Bill slowly. "I did not know if I would see you again."

"Ahoy, Bill," said Salty. "Ahoy, Bill."

Commander Gray came over to Bill and the others.

"It was good to see you come up out of the rescue chamber," he said. "Now that you are here, all the crew has been saved. Not one man was lost."

"That is something!" said Dan.

"With some sleep and good food we will be all right in no time," said Commander Gray.

"I am glad it is all over now," said Bill. "It was something to go through."

"It was all the men working together who saved us," said Commander Gray. "The Navy men on the rescue ships, in the rescue chamber, and on the *Sunfin*."

Then he looked at Dan.

"And it was the men on the *Sea Watch*, too," he said. "The Navy wants to thank you and all your men for your part in the rescue, Dan."

"We are glad we could do something to help," said Dan. "The *Sea Watch* and all of us on it are always ready to answer the Navy's call."

58

# EXERCISES

*Chapter One*

# BILL'S LETTER

*Choose the right word or words for these sentences.*

1. The men of the *Sea Watch* were working with a
     a) submarine.
     b) torpedo detector.
     c) anchor.

2. Dan and Carlos were
     a) cooks.
     b) Navy men.
     c) divers.

3. Diving for a torpedo was something the men of
the *Sea Watch*
     a) had not done.
     b) had done many times.
     c) would not do.

4. The men were looking for a torpedo that had been
     a) shot at the *Sea Watch*.
     b) found on the deck.
     c) used to train men.

5. Andy said he would not like to work on a
     a) boat.
     b) submarine.
     c) torpedo detector.

6. Bill could tell the men about submarines for he had been
   a) in the Navy.
   b) in a torpedo.
   c) on a diving boat.

7. The men laughed at Andy, but
   a) not one of them liked him.
   b) all of them liked him very much.
   c) one of them liked him.

8. When Dan found the torpedo, he
   a) shot it off.
   b) hooked a cable on it.
   c) left it.

9. Carlos called the Navy base and said the *Sea Watch* had found the last
   a) parrot.
   b) submarine.
   c) torpedo.

10. Back at the Navy base, Commander Gray held up a letter for
    a) Salty.
    b) Bill.
    c) Dan.

## Chapter Two

# ANDY RUNS THE SEA WATCH

*Choose the right word or words for these sentences.*

1. Bill was called back into the Navy to work on a
   a) torpedo boat.
   b) diving boat.
   c) submarine.

2. Commander Gray said the *Sunfin* was
   a) the best submarine.
   b) not a very good submarine.
   c) not his submarine.

3. Commander Gray asked Bill to help him
   a) find a torpedo.
   b) train men.
   c) pull up an anchor.

4. Bill said he would
   a) not like to go on the *Sunfin*.
   b) like to go on the *Sunfin*.
   c) not go on the *Sunfin*.

5. With Bill at work for the Navy, Andy would have to
   a) dive.
   b) work on the *Sunfin*.
   c) run the *Sea Watch*.

6. Andy said he could
   a) not run the *Sea Watch*.
   b) run the boat just the way Bill did.
   c) only cook on the *Sea Watch*.


7. Bill told the men he had to go to work on the *Sunfin*
   a) in the morning.
   b) after a long time.
   c) in a day or so.


8. When Andy ran the motor very fast, the *Sea Watch*
   a) went out fast from the dock.
   b) moved slowly from the dock.
   c) moved into the dock.


9. Andy saw that Carlos had
   a) let down the anchor.
   b) stopped the motor.
   c) left the boat.


10. When Andy started the boat up fast in the water, Carlos
    a) went into the water.
    b) laughed.
    c) let the anchor down.

## Chapter Three

# THE SUNFIN IN TROUBLE

*Choose the right word or words for these sentences.*

1. The men on a submarine
   a) eat and sleep at one time.
   b) have much room to work in.
   c) do not have much room to work in.

2. Bill was to stand watch in his place in the
   a) stern.
   b) bow.
   c) torpedo room.

3. The men with Commander Gray on the deck of the *Sunfin* were
   a) divers.
   b) cooks.
   c) lookouts.

4. When the *Sunfin* was ready to dive, Commander Gray said to radio the
   a) lookouts.
   b) *Sea Watch.*
   c) Navy base.

5. Before a submarine dives, all men must be
   a) on the deck.
   b) off the deck.
   c) in the water.

6. Signal lights in a submarine tell when
    a) the men are inside.
    b) air is escaping.
    c) all openings are closed.


7. Commander Gray looked at the gauge to see
    a) the radio.
    b) if the telephone was working.
    c) if air was escaping.


8. When Commander Gray heard the message on the telephone,
    a) he laughed.
    b) a look of worry came over him.
    c) he said to dive deeper.


9. Something must have gone wrong in the stern with one of the
    a) vents.
    b) torpedoes.
    c) lookouts.


10. After Commander Gray told the crew to take the *Sunfin* back to the top, the
    a) water stopped coming in.
    b) crew pumped out the water.
    c) submarine started going down again.

*Chapter Four*

# THE SEA WATCH TO THE RESCUE

*Choose the right word or words for these sentences.*

1. The Navy asked all ships to
    a) find a torpedo.
    b) train men.
    c) help save the crew of the *Sunfin.*

2. Dan's message back to the Navy said,
    a) SEA WATCH CANNOT HELP.
    b) SEA WATCH READY TO HELP.
    c) SEA WATCH NEEDS HELP.

3. The first thing Commander Gray let up from the *Sunfin* was a
    a) torpedo.
    b) smoke signal.
    c) telephone buoy.

4. The crew of the *Sunfin* shot smoke signals from a
    a) telephone.
    b) gun.
    c) torpedo.

5. Carlos had trouble seeing the smoke signals as
    a) fog came in.
    b) no smoke signals went off.
    c) they went back to the Navy base.

6. Commander Gray saw that
    a) all of his men had escaped.
    b) not one of his men had escaped.
    c) only some of his men had escaped.


7. Commander Gray told his men to
    a) run around the submarine.
    b) talk if they wanted to.
    c) not talk if they did not have to.


8. The men in the *Sunfin* first knew a boat had come
   when they heard
    a) Dan on the telephone.
    b) a diver walking on the deck.
    c) the motor of the *Sea Watch*.


9. The men of the *Sunfin* hoped to escape with
    a) a helmet.
    b) an escape lung.
    c) a diving suit.


10. The last man who swam up from the escape
    chamber was
    a) Bill.
    b) Commander Gray.
    c) the radio man of the *Sunfin*.

*Chapter Five*

# THE STORM

*Choose the right word or words for these sentences.*

1. The rescue commander said the other members of the *Sunfin* crew could be in the
   a) stern.
   b) buoy.
   c) water.

2. The Navy was going to try and save the other members of the *Sunfin's* crew with the
   a) escape lung.
   b) rescue chamber.
   c) torpedo detector.

3. The Navy needed Dan to
   a) go into the rescue chamber.
   b) send signals.
   c) hook a cable on the *Sunfin*.

4. Andy started to worry that
   a) more fog would come in.
   b) a storm would come up.
   c) the air pump would stop.

5. Before he dived, Dan asked for a
   a) hammer.
   b) gauge.
   c) torpedo detector.

68

6. When Dan got down to the *Sunfin,* he
    a) pulled his rope.
    b) looked for Bill.
    c) hooked on the cable.

7. The message tapped back from the men inside the *Sunfin* said,
    a) TAKE YOUR TIME.
    b) AIR GOING FAST.
    c) WE DON'T WANT HELP.

8. Dan pulled four times on his rope to let Carlos know that
    a) Bill was all right.
    b) a message had been tapped to him.
    c) he was through diving.

9. As he was pulled up, Dan stopped from time to time
    a) to get used to the new air pressure.
    b) to hook cables.
    c) to tap messages.

10. Carlos said the rescue chamber
    a) could not go down in a storm.
    b) was gone.
    c) was out of air.

## Chapter Six

# LAST MAN UP FROM THE SUNFIN

*Choose the right word or words for these sentences.*

1. As the storm started up, the men on the ships
    a) put lines around things on the decks.
    b) went back to the Navy base.
    c) went down in the rescue chamber.

2. Down in the *Sunfin*, the men
    a) knew a storm had come up.
    b) could not tell a storm had come up.
    c) came up with escape lungs.

3. The men on the *Sea Watch* were worrying about
    a) how much air was left in the *Sunfin*.
    b) the cable on the hatch.
    c) how the Navy rescue chamber would work.

4. In the morning, the storm
    a) went on.
    b) was gone.
    c) started again.

5. Four anchor buoys held the
    a) *Sunfin*.
    b) *Sea Watch*.
    c) rescue ship.

6. When all of the cable had been pulled up into the rescue chamber, the chamber was
   a) by the ship.
   b) in the mud.
   c) over the escape hatch on the *Sunfin*.

7. The rescue chamber could take
   a) some of the men left in the *Sunfin*.
   b) all of the men left in the *Sunfin*.
   c) four of the men left in the *Sunfin*.

8. The men inside the rescue chamber
   a) had to worry about the bends.
   b) had the bends.
   c) did not have to worry about the bends.

9. When the hatch on the rescue chamber was opened, the last man to come out was
   a) Bill.
   b) Commander Gray.
   c) Dan.

10. Commander Gray said that
    a) some of the *Sunfin's* crew had been saved.
    b) all of the *Sunfin's* crew had been saved.
    c) part of the *Sunfin's* crew had been saved.

# VOCABULARY

*Submarine Rescue*, the third book in the *Deep-Sea Adventure Series*, uses a vocabulary of 289 different words for a total of 8494 running words. All but 85 words, which are italicized in the list below, may be considered basic vocabulary words. *Submarine Rescue* repeats 210 words from the first and second books of the series, *The Sea Hunt* and *Treasure under the Sea* respectively, while adding 79 new ones.

| | | | | |
|---|---|---|---|---|
| a | *cable* | find | *hose* | more |
| about | call | first | how | morning |
| after | came | fish | | *motor* |
| again | can | *float* | I | *move* |
| *ahoy* | *cannot* | *fog* | if | much |
| air | Carlos | food | in | *mud* |
| all | *chamber* | for | *inside* | must |
| always | close | found | into | my |
| am | *code* | four | is | |
| an | come | from | it | *Navy* |
| *anchor* | coming | fun | it's | need |
| and | *commander* | | | new |
| Andy | *cook* | *gauge* | just | no |
| another | could | get | | not |
| *answer* | *crew* | give | keep | now |
| any | | glad | *knew* | |
| are | Dan | go | know | of |
| around | *dark* | gone | | off |
| as | day | good | last | on |
| *ask* | *deck* | got | laugh | one |
| at | *deep* | gray | left | only |
| away | *deeper* | great | let | open |
| | *detector* | gun | let's | or |
| back | did | | letter | other |
| bag | *dive* | had | light | our |
| *base* | *diver* | *hammer* | like | out |
| be | *diving* | has | *line* | over |
| been | do | *hatch* | long | |
| before | *dock* | have | look | *parrot* |
| *bends* | done | he | *lookout* | part |
| best | don't | heard | *lung* | place |
| big | down | *heavy* | | *pressure* |
| Bill | | *held* | made | *pull* |
| boat | eat | *hello* | make | *pump* |
| *bottom* | enough | *helmet* | man | put |
| *bow* | *escape* | help | many | |
| *breathe* | *escaping* | here | me | *radio* |
| brought | every | him | *member* | ran |
| *buoy* | | his | men | ready |
| but | far | *hook* | *message* | real |
| by | fast | hope | minute | *rescue* |

72

| | | | | |
|---|---|---|---|---|
| right | so | *tanks* | took | watch |
| room | some | *tap* | top | water |
| *rope* | something | *telephone* | *torpedo* | way |
| run | soon | tell | train | we |
| | *sound* | thank | *trapped* | went |
| said | *splash* | that | *trouble* | were |
| Salty | *stand* | that's | *tube* | what |
| *save* | *start* | the | two | when |
| saw | *stern* | them | | where |
| *sea* | *stood* | then | under | who |
| see | *stop* | there | up | why |
| *ship* | *storm* | they | us | will |
| *shot* | *submarine* | thing | use | with |
| should | suit | this | | work |
| side | sun | three | *vent* | *worry* |
| *signal* | Sunfin | through | very | would |
| *sir* | *sunk* | time | | *wrong* |
| sleep | *swam* | to | wait | |
| *slowly* | | together | walk | yes |
| small | take | told | want | you |
| smoke | talk | too | was | your |

73